HACKBACK

THE COMPUTER MUSICAL
Robert Hyman

Note to Producer:

A licence is required to perform this work. Please address your application to Education Dept., International Music Publications, Woodford Trading Estate, Southend Road, Woodford Green, Essex IG8 8HN, stating the title of the work and the proposed dates of performance.

Duration: ACT 1 — 60 minutes
ACT 2 — 45 minutes

Edited by BARRIE CARSON TURNER

First Published 1989
© International Music Publications

Exclusive Distributors
International Music Publications
Southend Road, Woodford Green,
Essex IG8 8HN, England.

215-2-557

NOTES ON PERFORMANCE

CASTING

There are lots of parts for everybody and many of them can either be male or female (Chrys can be Chrystopher or Chrystine, for example). Those parts that have been deliberately written as male or female (and where it is not obvious by character name, etc.) are indicated in the cast list.

STAGING

The staging is planned around three areas. The largest and central area is inside the computer of Chrys String. The set should look as metallic as possible. If you can, add lots of little flashing lights (borrow a rope light from your local disco). Try to make everything look as hi-tech as possible.

To turn the central area into the Space Bar just add a sign, a price list, and perhaps a Hexadecimal waiter.

The Data Chute should be a large square panel in the back wall/backcloth, rather like a cat-flap, though a plank used a slide going off-stage will suffice.

Stage right is the Laboratory, if possible on a stage extension. Keep it stylised. No walls, lots of papers, some equipment (borrow this from the science department), a telephone, and of course a computer. The Sonic Demodulator need be no more than a cardboard box made to look like the most complicated and interesting piece of equipment there, preferably with the words 'Sonic Demodulator' clearly written on it.

Stage left is the String front room, again if possible on a stage extension. Keep it simple — a table and chairs, a sofa, (three chairs with a cover over the top), a telephone with second extension telephone, and a computer is all that is needed. (In the film scene the Strings should *mime* watching the TV.)

If possible use real computers on the set, though again cardboard boxes will do nicely. Computer programs specially written to fit in with the action of the play would add considerable interest. In order to help the audience, when the computers are used in the show, the Graphics could hold up cards which say what is being typed. A shoebox, next to each computer will represent the modem into which the phone is plugged.

COSTUMES

The humans look ordinary. Dr Crow and Ms Demeanour both wear lab coats. Ms Demeanour has her hair up and wears glasses.

The Components are bright and metallic — use lots of luminous colours. Colour-code friendship groups by using several stripes of horizontal colour. Don't forget to stripe the face and hair.

Cursor wears pyjamas in Act 1, Scene 4.

The Hexadecimals look as revolting as possible, either *totally* blue or red, and have lots of tentacles and bits hanging off them. Try to make them look as if they have ten of everything.

Daisy Wheel should look very feminine and have as many costume changes as possible. Lots of flowing dresses and shoulder pads. Claire, Patsy and Eustace are three characters in one costume, and wear the initials C.P.U.

LIGHTING

The three areas should be lit separately. Green light should be used on the central area whenever the computer is 'working'. (But the Space Bar should use pretty pink lighting.) Use special effects for the hackback scene, either a strobe or a mirror ball, or again something borrowed from your local disco. The ballet in Act 2 between Dr Crow and Ms Demeanour will certainly benefit from a smoke machine. A follow spot will be useful to light entrances from the back of the hall.

SOUND

The cassette included with this book contains a selection of sound effects to use with the show.

Musically, most of the numbers have a strong beat, so if possible include drums with the piano. The addition of keyboards will add the possibility of further electronic effects.

As the show is set in three areas, it is unlikely there will be any long scene changes, but if the need should arrive don't forget to let the band fill in, to cover.

PROPS

The following props are as mentioned in the dialogue. Any number of others, however, may be used to enhance the look of the show. Feel free!

Laboratory scene	Inside the computer	String front room
Tea trolley & tea things	Lunch box	Box of tissues
Tea bags	Arm sling *(for Calli)*	Saucepan
Kettle or urn	Banana	Tea-towel
Biscuits	3 Coshes	Rubber gloves
Glass of 'electrolyte solution' *(water with green food colouring)*	Torches	Apron
	Drinks *(Space Bar)*	Dinner things
Aprons	Chains *(for Mandi)*	Tea cosy
	Kazoos	Pipe
	Garlands of flowers	Vase of flowers
	2 Medals *(presentation scene)*	Can of soft drink
	Tea trolleys & tea things	
	Biscuits	
	Bag of 'extra strong mints'	
	Whistles	
	4 Food sacks	
	2 Balaclavas	

FRONT OF HOUSE

Use computers as much as possible in the design of the show — for tickets and posters, etc. Try and turn your hall into a computer, so that the audience really feel that they too are *Inside the Machine*.

NOTES

Substitute the reference Tab makes to Brent Cross (in the scene with the Smalltalks) with a shopping centre near to your school.

The HACKBACK! reprise at the beginning of Act 2 (Music No. 17) should be shorter than its counterpart at the close of Act 1.

MUSICAL NUMBERS

ACT 1

No.			V/S Page	Lib Page
1	OVERTURE	*Instrumental*	5	6
2	INSIDE THE MACHINE	Components	10	6
3	FILM MUSIC	*Instrumental*	16	9
4	HARK WHO'S TALKING	*Chrys, Tab, Len, Val*	19	10
5	MANDI'S TUNE	*Instrumental*	25	13
6	DAISY'S ULTIMATE AIM MUSIC	*Instrumental*	26	15
7	WHERE THERE'S A WHEEL THERE'S A WAY	Daisy, Rom, Ram	27	16
8	THE KITCHEN SINK BLUES	Len, Val	31	19
9	HACKBACK!	Components	34	25
10	HACKBACK! *(Reprise)*	Components	34	27
11	INSIDE THE MACHINE *(Reprise)*	*Instrumental*	10	28
12	DR CROW, WE WELCOME YOU	Chrys, Components	39	29
13	HACKBACK! *(Reprise)*	Chrys, Components	34	31
14	HACKBACK! *(Reprise)*	*Instrumental*	41	31

ACT 2

No.			V/S Page	Lib Page
15	OPENING MUSIC	*Instrumental*	41	32
16	DR CROW, WE WELCOME YOU *(Reprise)*	ALL	39	32
17	HACKBACK! *(Reprise)*	ALL	34	32
18	THE HEXADECIMAL DUMP	Hexadecimals	44	33
19	HE'S A CHICK PEA TYPE OF GUY	Ms Demeanour, Rose Hip	51	37
20	I'M ROM. I'M RAM.	Rom, Ram, Hexadecimals	55	39
21	FANFARE	*Instrumental*	58	42
22	FANFARE *(Reprise)*	*Instrumental*	58	42
23	FOOD FOR THOUGHT	Chip, Chrys, Hexadecimals	59	42
24	THE HEXADECIMAL DUMP *(Reprise)*	ALL	64	43
25	OUTSIDE THE MACHINE	Chip, Chrys, Components	65	44
26	HACKBACK! *(Reprise)*	ALL	34	47

CAST

HUMANS - *Screenside*

CHRYS STRING	Computer mad. Very likeable.
TAB(itha) STRING	Sister of Chrys. A bit of a tomboy who gets bored easily.
LEN STRING VAL STRING	Mother and Father of Chrys and Tab. They love their children and the TV — but not in that order.
DR MICHAEL CROW	Very handsome, but slightly dense hero.
MS DEMEANOUR	Seemingly dull and unattractive lab assistant but quite the opposite in the end.
ROSE HIP	The tea-lady. She makes the worst cup of tea you have ever tasted. She is also tone deaf.
AGNES SMALLTALK CYRIL SMALLTALK	Nosy neighbours.
MEL(anie) STEVE *(a know-all)*	Friends of Chrys and Tab.
THIEF	A despicable creature — responsible for the most dastardly deed of the century....

COMPONENTS - *Inside the Machine*

CHIP	Narrator. Cheerful. Gets on with everybody.
VOLTAGE (m)	A powerful character.
CALLI (f)	A Graphic. Pretty, cheeky, and a bit of a wit.
BYTE NYBBLE	Best friends of Chip. Always hungry. They'll eat anything, and often do.
CLAIRE CENTRAL (f) PATSY PROCESSING (f) EUSTACE UNIT (m)	The C.P.U. The boss. Eustace suffers a great deal of henpecking from the other two.
DAISY WHEEL (f)	Not your typical villain — but a thoroughly nice girl and global megalomaniac.
ROM (m) RAM (m)	Henchmen to Daisy Wheel. Very tough, like night-club bouncers. They live in a world of proverbs and catchphrases.
CURSOR (m)	Does so!
GRAPH (m)	Short and cute. A trainee graphic.
MANDI (m)	A program. Definately a man, and one all the girls want to watch.
PC CONSTABLE	Slightly batty.
PHOTO (m) PHONO (f) REPRO (f)	Graphics.
CHOMPER (m) SALIVA (f)	Hexadecimals — Game Show contestants.
4 ASSISTANTS	Hexadecimals who assist at the Game Show.
GEO (m)	A Graphic. Non-speaking part doubling Steve.
BIBLIO (f)	A Graphic. Non-speaking part doubling Mel.
LITHO (m)	A Graphic. Non-speaking part doubling Cyril Smalltalk.
BIO (f)	A Graphic. Non-speaking part doubling Agnes Smalltalk.
GRAPHICS	Chorus goodies (any number).
HEXADECIMALS	Chorus baddies — the most horrible creatures you can imagine (any number).

ACT 1

OVERTURE
(1)

8

INSIDE THE MACHINE
(2, 11)

1st CUE: *Full lights on centre stage.* COMPONENTS *move forward.*
2nd CUE: CHIP: Inside the machine.

14

FILM MUSIC
(3)

CUE: TAB: Let's watch it then, eh?

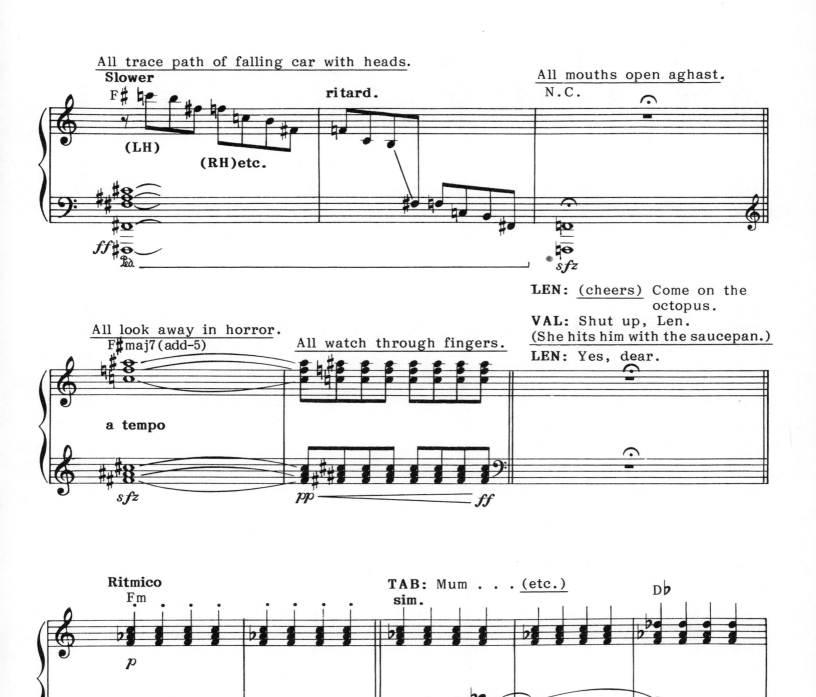

All trace path of falling car with heads.

Slower

ritard.

All mouths open aghast.
N.C.

LEN: (cheers) Come on the octopus.
VAL: Shut up, Len.
(She hits him with the saucepan.)
LEN: Yes, dear.

All look away in horror.
F#maj7(add-5)

a tempo

All watch through fingers.

Ritmico
Fm

TAB: Mum . . . (etc.)
sim.

Db

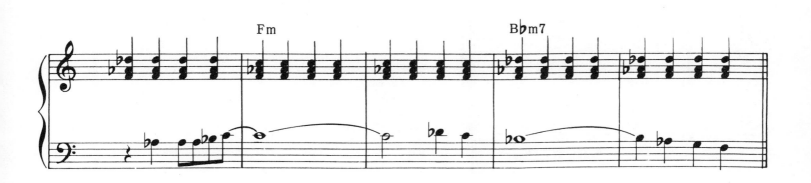

Fm

Bbm7

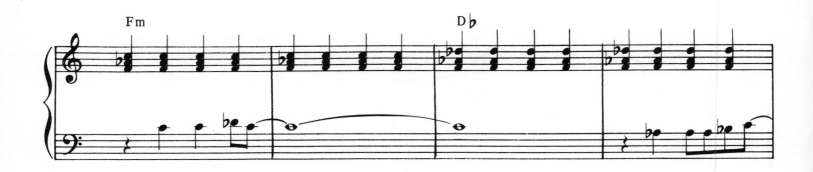

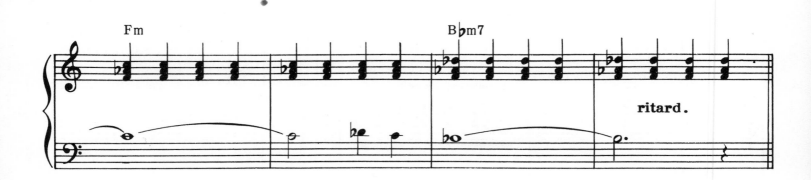

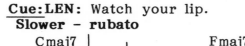

Cue:LEN: Watch your lip.
Slower – rubato

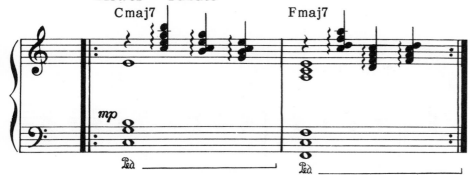

Repeat till next cue.

Cue:TAB: Oh no, they're going to kiss.
(Music wait for a moment, then...)
Very fast

Repeat ad lib.
Cut off on:
Cue: VAL: Well, this is going off right now.

HARK WHO'S TALKING
(4)

CUE: VAL: What have you got to say for yourself?

Argumentative; moderate speed (♩=148)

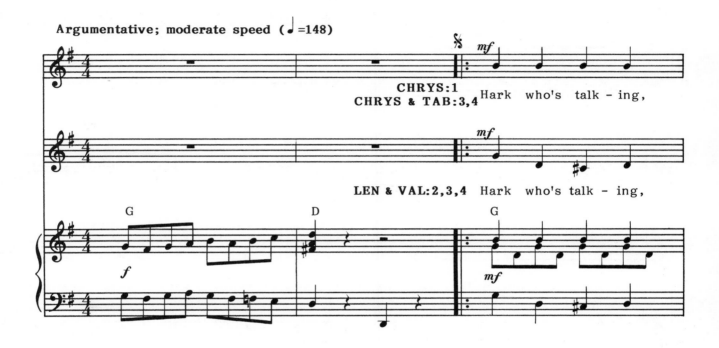

CHRYS:1
CHRYS & TAB:3,4 Hark who's talk - ing,

LEN & VAL:2,3,4 Hark who's talk - ing,

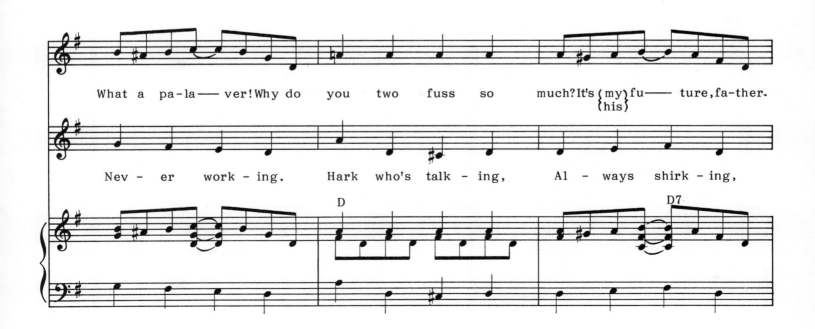

What a pa-la——ver! Why do you two fuss so much? It's {my}{his} fu—— ture, fa-ther.

Nev - er work - ing. Hark who's talk - ing, Al - ways shirk - ing,

23

MANDI'S TUNE
(5)

Slow, mysterious

1st CUE: ROSE HIP *picks up the phone and* DR CROW *stabs a button.*

2nd CUE: DR CROW *types, and presses the return button.*

3rd CUE: VAL *(Enters and picks up the phone):* Hello?

4th CUE: LEN *(Takes receiver out of VAL's hand and puts it to his ear:* Hello?

5th CUE: MANDI: All right, you win.

6th CUE: MANDI: First, I reconnect with the computer.

DAISY'S ULTIMATE AIM MUSIC
(6)

CUE: DAISY: IT is my *Ultimate Aim.*

Oh, my Ultimate Aim...

My Ultimate Aim...

The Ultimate Aim of Daisy Wheel...

The Ultimate Aim of Daisy Wheel, global megalomaniac and the most thoroughly nice girl you could ever wish to meet...

is...

WHERE THERE'S A WHEEL THERE'S A WAY

(7)

CUE: DAISY: Because I, Daisy Wheel, say so, and because where there's a Wheel there's a way.

DAISY WHEEL: Don't be down-heart-ed—— if your roll-ing—— stone has moss, For
DAISY WHEEL: Don't be down-heart-ed—— if a cop-per—— taps your phone, As

an-y de-cent bad-die —— will nev-er make a loss. It's
they live in glass hous-es —— and we have got a stone To

not an ap-ple but a bribe that keeps the—— fuzz at bay.
steal what-ev-er they have saved up for that—— rain-y day.

28

+ R & R: Where there's a Wheel ———————— there's a way.
+ R & R: Where there's a Wheel ———————— there's a way.

ROM & RAM: All that glit-ters is not gold but

pro-bab-ly worth nick-ing. Sticks and stones will break your bones but not as good as

kick-ing. A friend in need's a pest in-deed, one bit-ten is twice shy.

Bright – quasi Russian (♩ = ♪)
Poco a poco accellerando

30

THE KITCHEN SINK BLUES
(8)

CUE: CHRYS *(types):* 'Sing and dance'.

HACKBACK!
(9, 10, 13, 17, 26)

1st CUE: EUSTACE: Get Dr Crow!
2nd/3rd CUE: GRAPH: Did you say *Hackback?*
(Note: For the 2nd Cue *first* verse and *last* chorus only.)
4th CUE: CHIP: And then this happened:
5th CUE: GRAPH: Did you say *Hackback?*

Fast - get down and boogie! (♩=170)

VOLTAGE: It's time to take the test ———————— of Time, ——
CALLI: Don't back a-way from this, ———————— my friend, ——
CHIP: You have-n't giv-en me ———————— much choice, ——

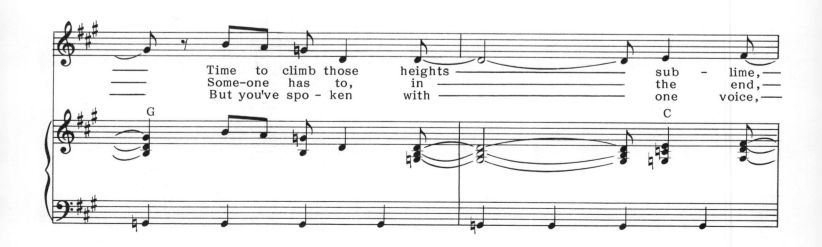

—— Time to climb those heights ———————————— sub - lime, ——
—— Some-one has to, in ———————————— the end, ——
—— But you've spo - ken with ———————————— one voice, ——

DR CROW, WE WELCOME YOU
(12, 16)

1st CUE: BYTE: Here they come.
2nd CUE: CHIP: Welcome back. If you remember, at the end of Act 1, this happened:

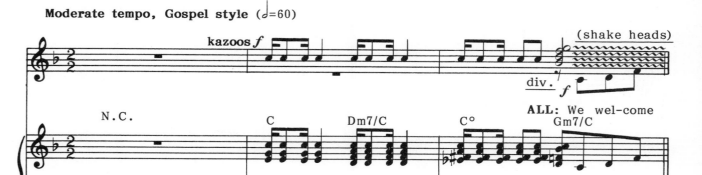

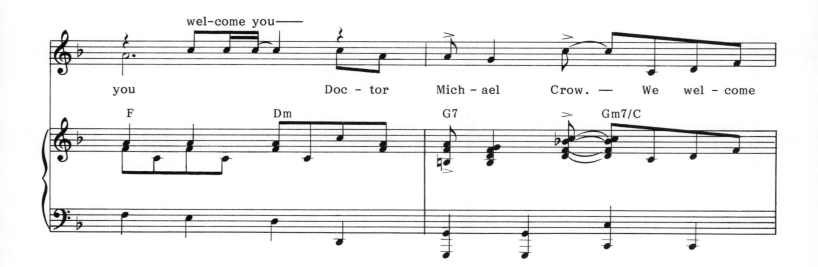

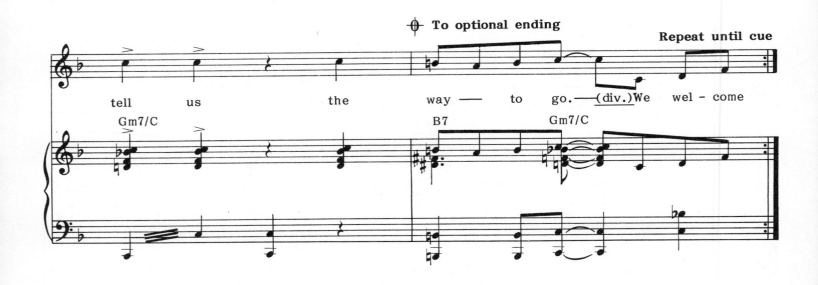

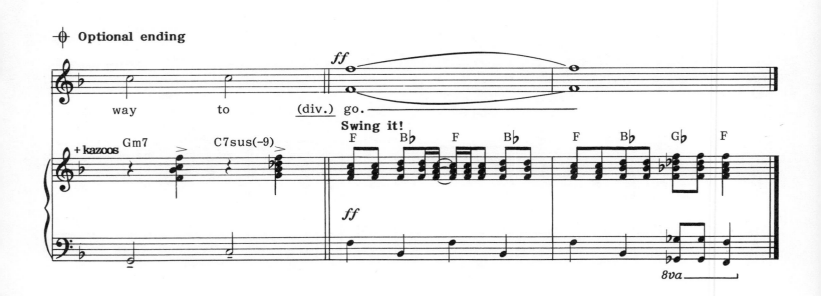

HACKBACK! *(Reprise)*
(14)

CUE: CHIP: Find out after the interval of HACKBACK.

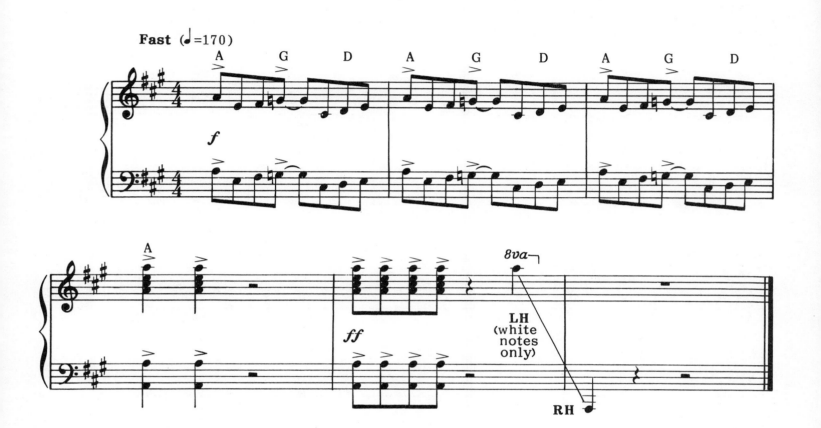

ACT 2

OPENING MUSIC
(15)

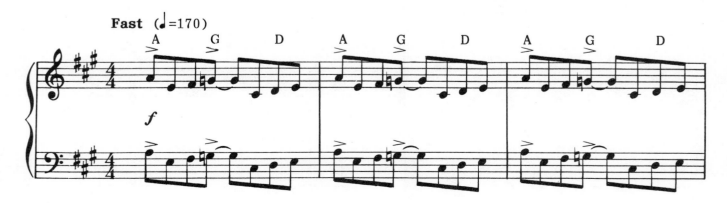

THE HEXADECIMAL DUMP
(18)

CUE: ROM & RAM: Oy, you lot. GET STUFFED!

Moderate tempo, heavy and menacing (♩=104)

Repeat till ready

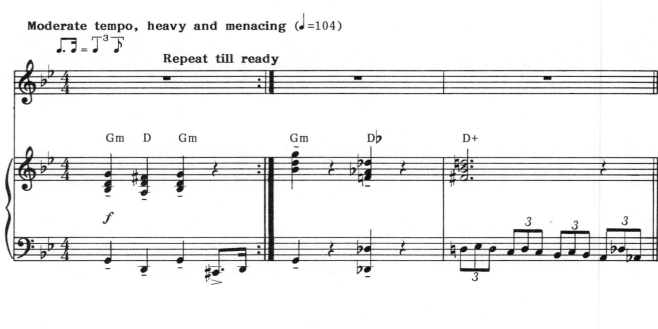

HEXADECIMALS: Which way leads— to glo-bal dev-as-ta-tion?
This way leads — you to your own des-truc-tion.

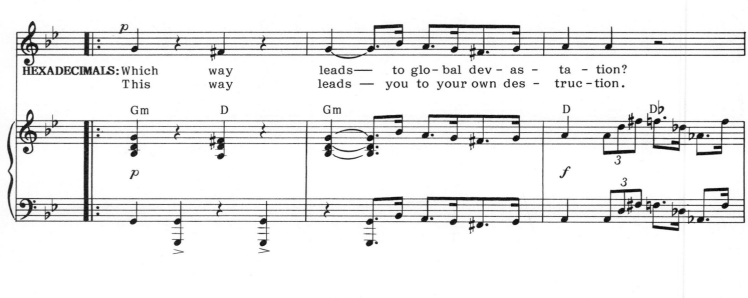

Which place holds— the ref-use of the world?
This place smells— so bad it makes you sick.

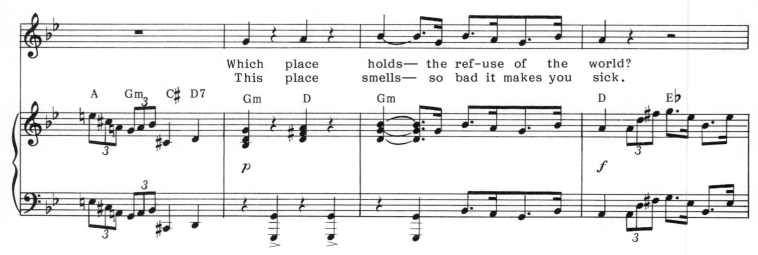

HE'S A CHICK-PEA TYPE OF GUY
(19)

CUE: MS DEMEANOUR: Exactly. He's a chick-pea type of guy.

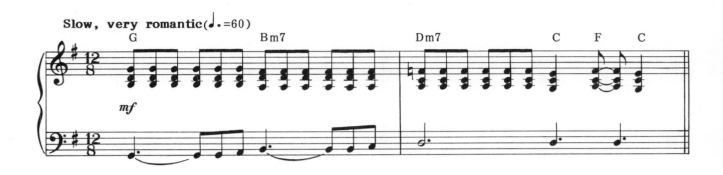

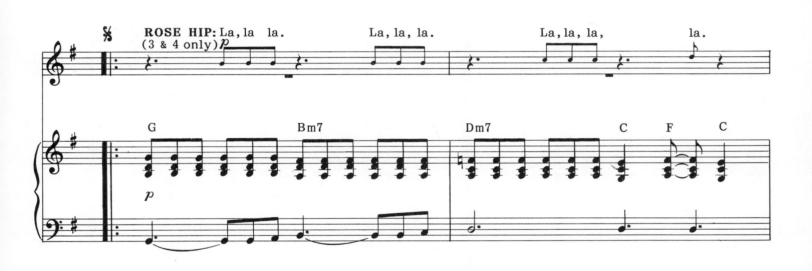

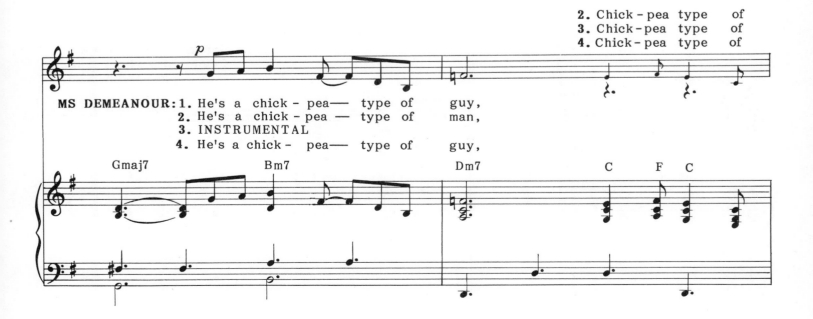

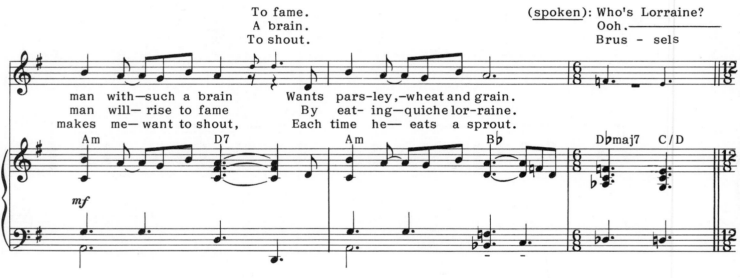

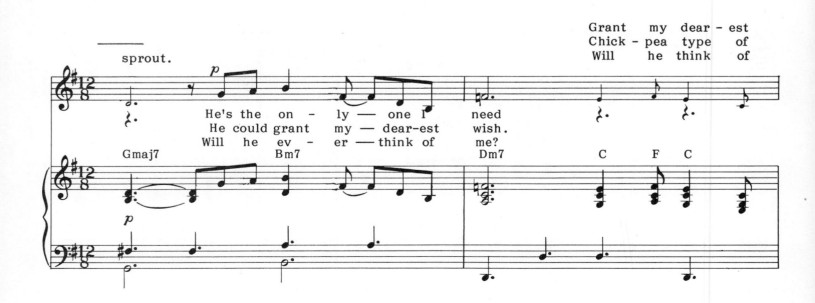

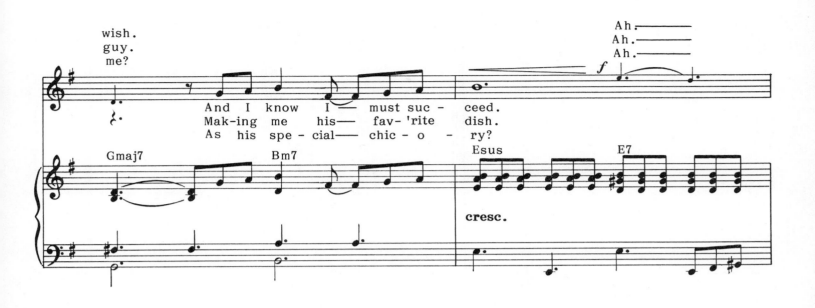

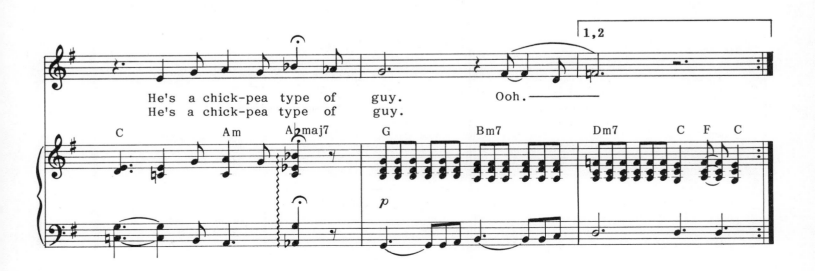

I'M ROM. I'M RAM.
(20)

CUE: *Lights up.*

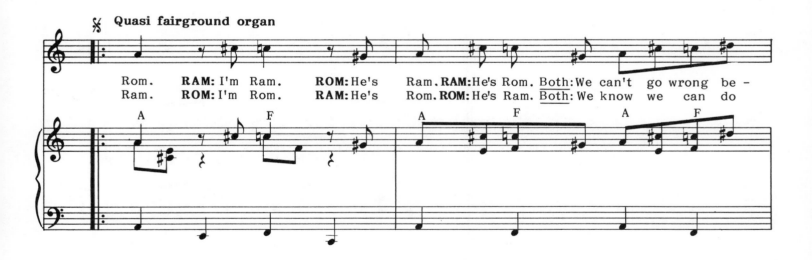

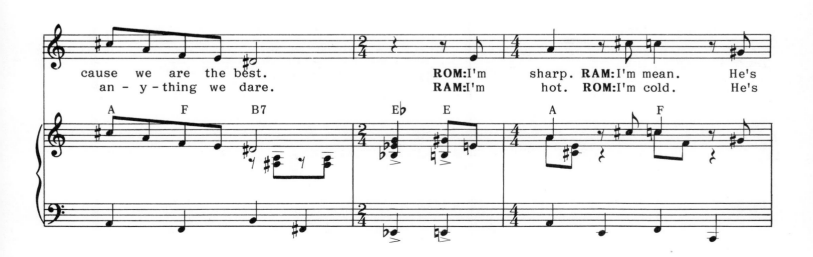

57

FANFARE
(21)

CUE: CHIP: Right then you lucky Hexadecimals, come on down!

Big and bouncy (♩=120)

FANFARE (*Reprise*)
(22)

1st CUE: CHIP: So, let's hear it for our two challengers tonight: Chomper and Saliva.
2nd CUE: CHIP: Our favourite game show guzzlers: Byte and Nybble.

Big and bouncy

FOOD FOR THOUGHT
(23)

CUE: CHIP: You have one minute starting...now!

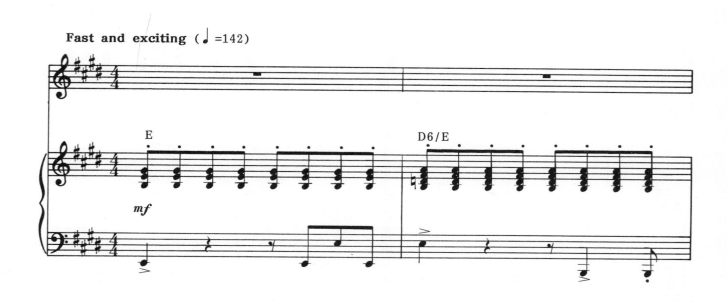

THE HEXADECIMAL DUMP (*Reprise*)
(24)

CUE: NYBBLE: To the Hexadecimal Dump.

OUTSIDE THE MACHINE
(25)

CUE: CHIP: We tell her. Your computer has great sound capabilities. She'll hear us.

Relaxed, not fast ($\quad$=120)

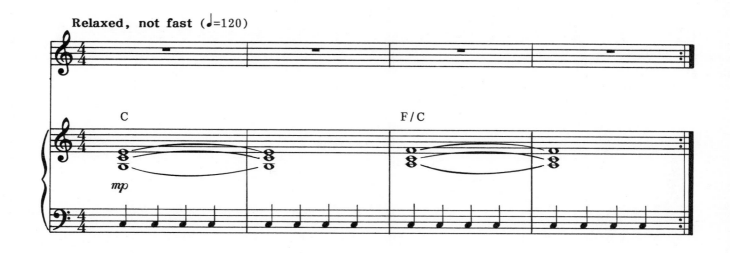

CHIP: Where d'you want — to go? — CHRYS: Screen-side. —

Will you show — me how — to go Screen-side? —

Printed by
Halstan & Co. Ltd., Amersham, Bucks., England